THE SILVEY-JEX PARTNERSHIP

DALESMAN

Dalesman Publishing Company
Stable Courtyard, Broughton Hall, Skipton, North Yorkshire BD23 3AE

First Edition 1997

© Silvey Jex Partnership1997

A British Library Cataloguing in Publication record is available for this book

ISBN 185568 115 3

Also by Silvey-Jex Outdoor Wreckreations (ISBN 1 85568 104 8)

Printed by Amadeus Press, Huddersfield

THE FUNNY SIDE OF GARDENING FROM SILVEY-JEX

ENCOURAGING WILDLIFE IS ALL VERY WELL, BUT I THINK YOU SPOIL THOSE FROGS.

....OKAY, NOW FOR A GENTLE FLOW OF WATER TURN THE KNOB TO THE 'RIGHT'-SORRY 'LEFT'

WHEN IT SAYS "TAKE OUT A DEEP TRENCH" YOUR GRANDAD DOESN'T DO THINGS BY HALF

HELLO...GARDENERS HELPLINE?

...BUT THE GOOD THING ABOUT THIS LITTLE CHAP IS, HE'S GOT A VERY STRONG ROOT SYSTEM

FOR GOODNESS SAKE MOTHER—WHAT AM I PAYING YOU FOR? SHOO THEM OFF! SHOO THEM OFF!

WAIT! STOP!! NOT AGAINST THE PLUM TREE.

GRANNY... LOOK WHAT FUNNY GRANDAD'S DOING

DON'T GO UP THERE JACK

AAHHH...RED HOT POKERS...MY FAVOURITE FLOWER

...AND THEY'VE ALL GOT COUNTRY NAMES MY DEARS...HERE'S DEVILS SCROTUM, GRANNYS KNICKERS, WHORES BOTTOM & OLD MANS PHLEGM.

FUNNY HOW ONE LITTLE WEED CAN RUIN A PERFECTLY GOOD LAWN

...AND WHAT MAKES YOU THINK THE CROWS ARE GOING TO CHOOSE YOUR GROW BAGS INSTEAD OF THE 14 ACRES OF CORN NOT HALF A MILE AWAY?

...AND AS YOU CAN SEE, THE PROPERTY HAS A SMALL, EASY TO MAINTAIN GARDEN...

WAIT A MINUTE...NO MY FAULT...I READ THE WRONG BIT...SORRY...IT SAYS
"ON NO ACCOUNT PRUNE THE HEADS"

...THEY KEEP THE LAWN TRIMMED, BUT OF COURSE YOU HAVE TO BE CAREFUL WHERE YOU TREAD

..ANYWAY WE HAD SOME TURF LEFT- SO I THOUGHT, SHAME TO THROW IT AWAY....

SO YOU'RE JUST GOING TO ROTAVATE THAT ONE SPOT THEN?

... WISH I'D NEVER BOUGHT HIM THAT THING.

BY HECK YOUNG NORMAN, THA'S BLOODY HEAVY HANDED WI' SECATEURS

WELL, WE CUT THE GRASS LIKE YOU SAID MISSUS....
BUT IT WEREN'T ARF A JOB

NORMAN - YOU KNOW THOSE PEOPLE YOU RANG ABOUT FENCING?

HERBERT...COULD YOU CEASE THE LAWN SPIKING WHILE WE HAVE TEA?

THERE! I WASN'T GOING TO LET ONE LITTLE DANDELION SPOIL MY LAWN!

IT'S GREAT... YOU PUT THE WORD OUT THAT THE WIFE'S GONE MISSING
AND BINGO! THEY COME ROUND AND TURN OVER YOUR GARDEN.

DO STOP MOANING WOMAN — THEY'RE BEDDING PLANTS AREN'T THEY?

JOYCE! REMEMBER THAT MUSHROOM SPAWN? ONLY ONE'S COME UP

SIGH, WHY HE HAS TO FINISH IT TONIGHT I DON'T KNOW... THE LAWN WILL STILL BE THERE IN THE MORNING

SAW.....CLAMP....SECATEURS.....

HE SAYS HE'S FEEDING THE FISH... BUT I'M NOT SO SURE

DOBSON...WOULD YOU MIND HANGING YOUR JACKET SOMEWHERE ELSE

GEORGE—WHEN ARE YOU GOING TO DO SOMETHING ABOUT THIS "RIGHT OF WAY" PROBLEM

IT'S YOUR OWN STUPID FAULT FOR TURFING OVER THE POND

DON'T GET STUPID, JUST BECAUSE MOTHER BEAT YOU TO THE BATHROOM AGAIN.

GOOD MORNING. WE'RE YOUR NEW NEIGHBOURS. I'M ADAM.. THIS IS MY WIFE EVE.

...: SO WE THOUGHT.. SEEING AS HE SPENT ALL HIS TIME HERE ....

YOU GET OFF TO WORK HENRY – I'LL DO THE WATERING

...AND THE PRIZE FOR THE BIGGEST PUMPKIN GOES POSTHUMOUSLY TO.....

KEVIN...I SAID GIVE GRANNY A <u>GENTLE</u> PUSH IN THE HAMMOCK

THE AD JUST SAID "FRESH MANURE - DELIVERED TO YOUR DOOR"

HMMM...NOT QUITE WHAT I EXPECTED FROM AN "OPEN TO THE PUBLIC" GARDEN

YOUR DAD NEVER WAS MUCH GOOD WITH ELECTRIC THINGS

MUM! GRAN'S GOT GREENFLY!

YOU DAMAGE THAT TREE MY BOY—AND YOU'RE IN BIG TROUBLE

IF YOU ASK ME YOU'VE WASTED YOUR MONEY

FOR HEAVEN'S SAKE HERBERT, IF IT'S NOT MANURE ON YOUR CLOTHES-IT'S OIL!

OH YES IT'S VERY COLOURFUL...I'VE GOT BROWN SPOT, GREEN FLY, WHITEFLY, BLACK FLY, YELLOW OPHION FLY, ORANGETIP CATERPILLERS RED SPIDER MITES AND BLUE BOTTLES.

LEFT A BIT,
DOWN A BIT,
TOO FAR, UP A BIT,
NO NOT THAT ONE
THE LEAF NEXT
TO IT, TUT, NO, NO...

SILVEY JEX.

HAVE YOU PUT MANURE IN THE WINDOW BOX AGAIN HERBERT?

I DON'T WANT TO BE PICKY ARTHUR BUT I THINK YOU'RE SPENDING TOO MUCH TIME IN THE VEGETABLE PATCH

THEY'RE OUT THERE, I KNOW THEY ARE, I CAN HEAR THEM
...YOU CAN'T TRUST SLUGS YOU KNOW